My Color Book

Mi libro de colores

SOUTHWESTERN

KINGFISHER
This edition published in 2011
by the Southwestern Company
by arrangement with Kingfisher

First published as *First Color Book* in 2003
Copyright © Kingfisher 2003

Library of Congress Cataloging-in-Publication Data
has been applied for.

ISBN 978-0-7534-6384-0

Printed in China

Illustrated by Mandy Stanley
Educational consultant: Ann Montague-Smith
Spanish translation: María del Pilar Gáñez

Contents / Índice

Suggestions for parents

Color is all around us, and young children respond to strong colors. Learning about colors—their names, the shades of a given color—is an important skill because so many things around us are recognized by their color such as oranges, lemons, and frogs. This bright, inviting book will be an invaluable aid to familiarizing your child with color names.

Very young children will enjoy browsing through the book and looking at the attractive pictures. Encourage them to talk about and name the things in the pictures and to say what colors they can see.

When you look at the book together, make it an enjoyable experience. Encourage your child to talk about the things that they can see, and name them together. Ask them to talk about the different shades of a color such as light blue, sky blue, and navy blue. Encourage them to find other examples of the color, or shade, elsewhere in the book. Ask your child to draw pictures of some of the things that they can see in the book and to color them, choosing the appropriate color.

Learning doesn't have to stop when the book is closed! Together, look at things in your home and outside, and talk about their colors. An ideal time to talk about color is when your child is getting dressed. You could ask what color shirt or socks they'd like to wear. When out shopping, look at the color of packages, vegetables, and fruits. At home, encourage your child to draw and color and talk with them about the chosen colors. Make repeating patterns with blocks or other toys, and encourage your child to name the colors chosen and to say what comes next.

Above all, remember that learning about color is fun!

Ann Montague-Smith

Ann Montague-Smith, Principal Lecturer in Primary Education
University College, Worcester, England

Sugerencias para los padres

El color está en todo lo que nos rodea y a los niños pequeños les encantan los colores fuertes. El aprendizaje de los colores—sus nombres o matices—es una aptitud muy importante. Es gracias al color que reconocemos muchas de las cosas que nos rodean; por ejemplo las naranjas, los limones y las ranas. Este libro, vistoso y atractivo, será de gran ayuda para que su hijo se familiarice con los nombres de los colores.

Los más pequeños disfrutarán mucho hojeando el libro y mirando los atractivos dibujos. Estimúlelos para que hablen sobre las cosas que ven, para que las nombren y digan qué colores tienen.

Cuando miren juntos el libro, trate de que sea una experiencia divertida. Aliente a su hijo a que le cuente qué cosas ve en el libro y digan juntos cómo se llaman. Pregúntele acerca de los diferentes tonos de algún color; por ejemplo, el azul claro, el azul marino y el azul oscuro. Anímelo a descubrir otros ejemplos de cada color o de un matiz del color en otras partes del libro. Pídale al niño que dibuje algunas de las cosas que ve en el libro y que las coloree del color que corresponde.

¡El niño puede seguir aprendiendo aunque no tenga el libro abierto! Miren juntos los objetos que están en casa y fuera de ella y hablen de los colores que tienen. Un momento ideal para hablar de los colores es la hora de vestirse. Podría preguntarle qué color de calcetines o de camisa le gustaría ponerse. Cuando vayan de compras, miren el color de los envases, las verduras y las frutas. En casa, aliente a su hijo a dibujar y colorear, y luego hablen sobre los colores que eligieron. También puede agrupar juguetes o bloques según el color o por secuencias de colores y pedirle que nombre un color y diga cuál viene después.

Pero lo más importante es que recuerde que aprender sobre los colores es muy divertido.

Ann Montague-Smith.

Ann Montague-Smith, jefa del departamento de educación primaria
University College, Worcester, Inglaterra

Meet the colors
Te presentamos los colores

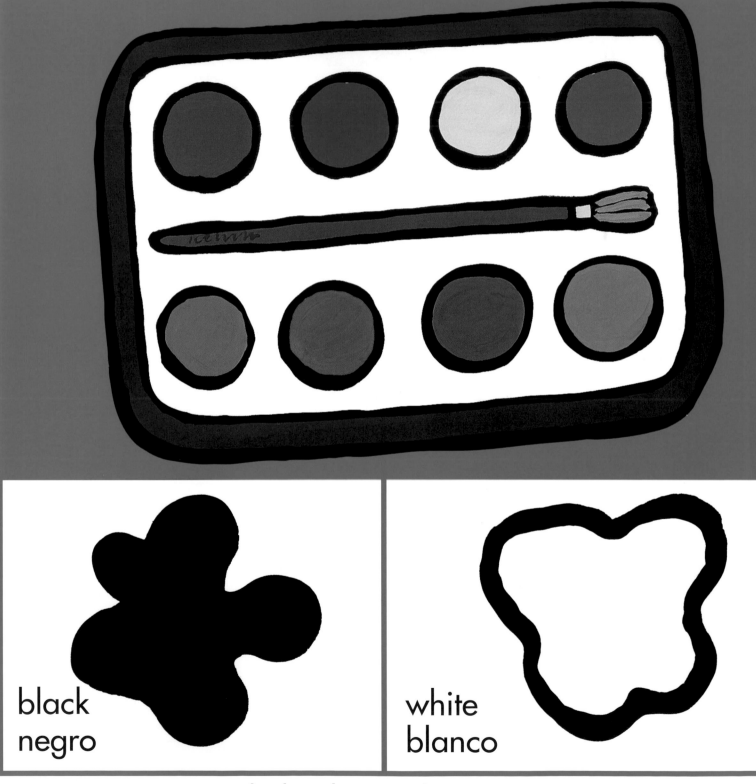

black
negro

white
blanco

Which color matches your eyes?
¿Cuál de estos colores se parece al de tus ojos?

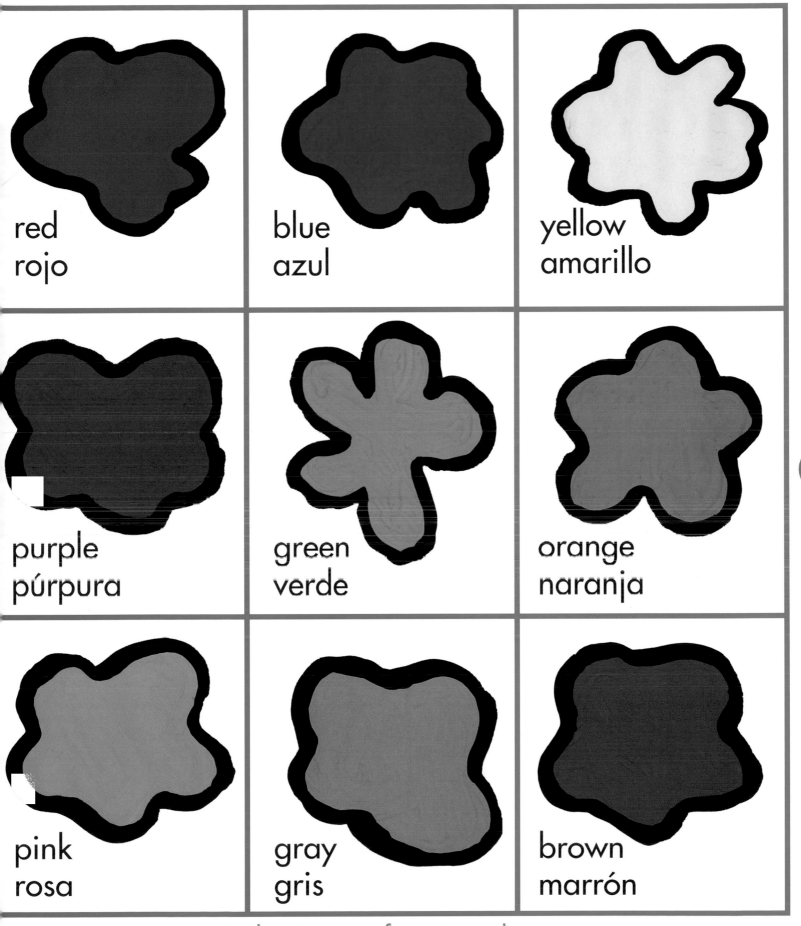

red
rojo

blue
azul

yellow
amarillo

purple
púrpura

green
verde

orange
naranja

pink
rosa

gray
gris

brown
marrón

7

What is your favorite color?
¿Cuál es tu color preferido?

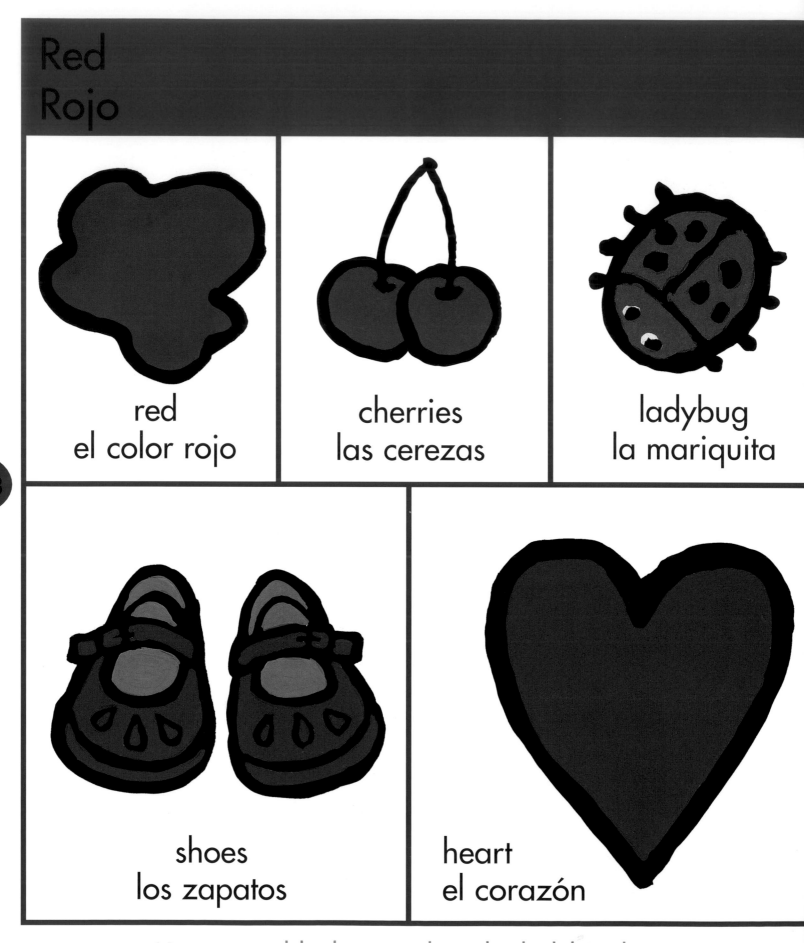

red
el color rojo

cherries
las cerezas

ladybug
la mariquita

shoes
los zapatos

heart
el corazón

8

How many black spots does the ladybug have?
¿Cuántas manchas negras tiene la mariquita?

balloon
el globo

strawberries
las fresas

blush
el rubor

dragon
el dragón

rose
la rosa

Which red things can you eat?
¿Qué cosas de color rojo se pueden comer?

Yellow
Amarillo

yellow
el color amarillo

sun
el sol

daffodil
el narciso

sandcastle
el castillo
de arena

moon and stars
la luna y las estrellas

How many stars can you see?
¿Cuántas estrellas ves?

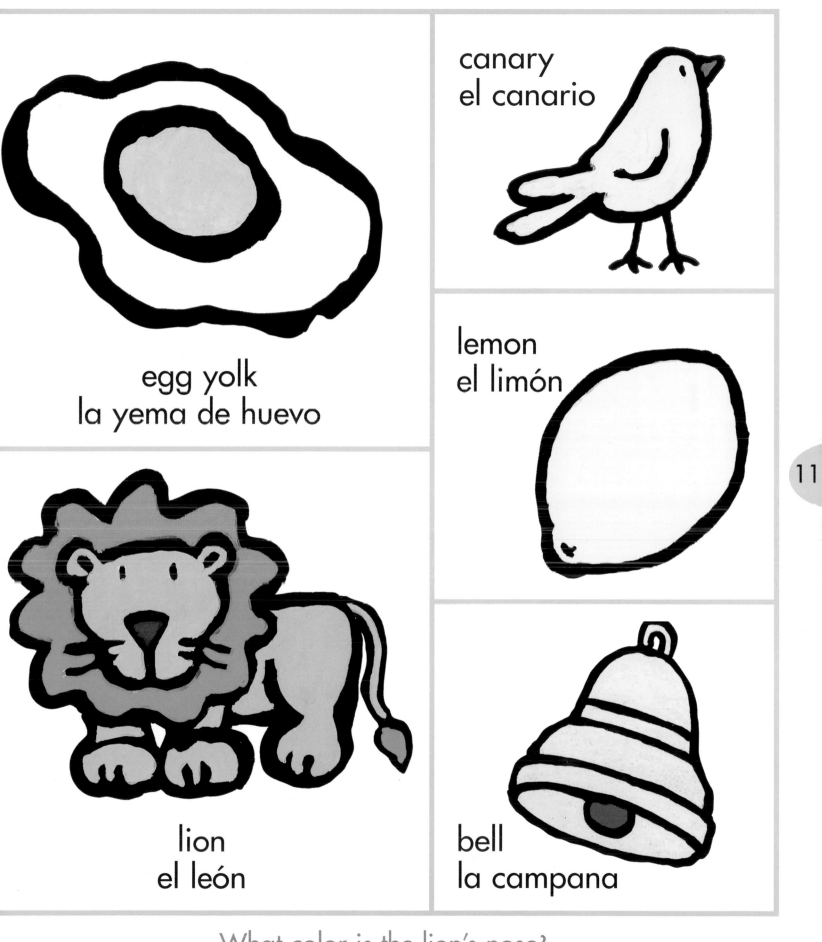

egg yolk
la yema de huevo

canary
el canario

lemon
el limón

lion
el león

bell
la campana

11

What color is the lion's nose?
¿De qué color es el hocico del león?

Blue
Azul

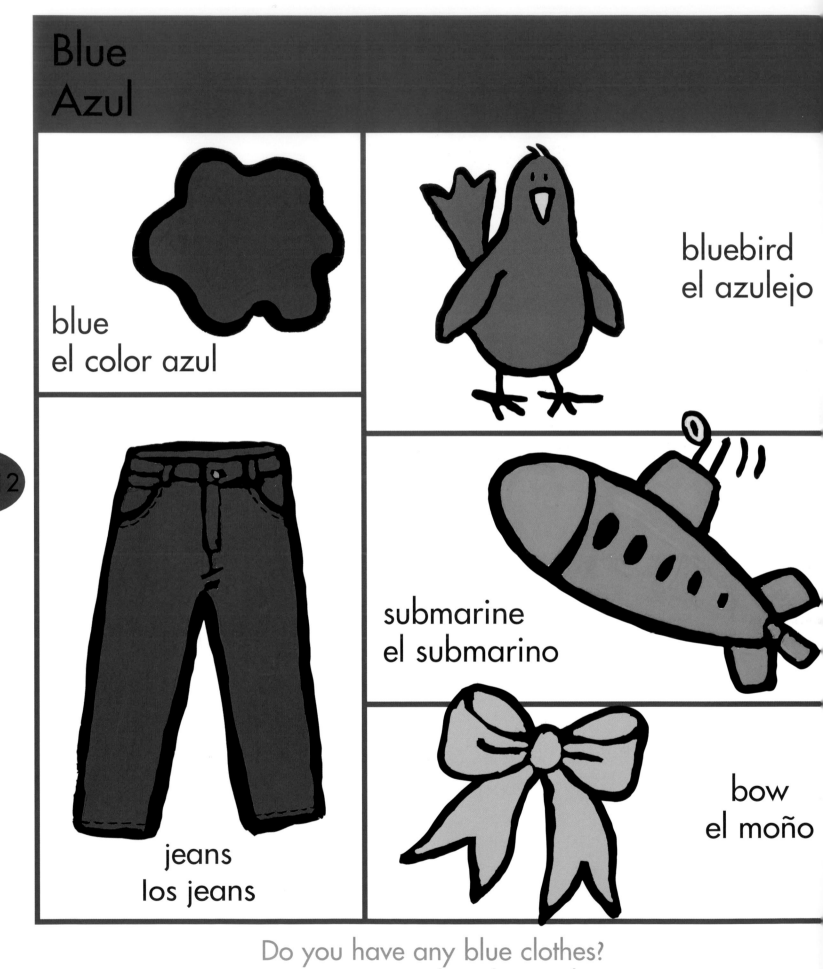

blue
el color azul

bluebird
el azulejo

submarine
el submarino

jeans
los jeans

bow
el moño

Do you have any blue clothes?
¿Tienes ropa de color azul?

12

swimming pool
la piscina

bluebells
los jacintos
silvestres

sneakers
los tenis

blue sky
el cielo azul

What shape is the window?
¿Qué forma tiene la ventana?

14

black
el color negro

blackboard el pizarrón

music
la música

cat
el gato

night sky
el cielo nocturno

What color are the cat's eyes?
¿De qué color son los ojos del gato?

witch
la bruja

blackberries
las moras

spider
la araña

gorilla
el gorila

How many legs does the spider have?
¿Cuántas patas tiene la araña?

White
Blanco

white
el color blanco

polar bear
el oso polar

milk
la leche

snowman
el muñeco de nieve

rabbit
el conejo

What color is the snowman's scarf?
¿De qué color es la bufanda del muñeco de nieve?

16

underwear
la ropa interior

clouds
las nubes

ghost
el fantasma

sheep
la oveja

bone
el hueso

Which of these white things do you wear?
¿De estas cosas blancas, cuáles usas para vestirte?

Green
Verde

green
el color verde

frog
la rana

grass
el pasto

cactus
el cactus

How many animals can you see in the grass?
¿Cuántos animales ves en el pasto?

18

lime
la lima

crocodile
el cocodrilo

leaf
la hoja

apple
la manzana

caterpillar
la oruga

backpack
la mochila

19

What color are the caterpillar's spots?
¿De qué color son las manchas de la oruga?

Pink
Rosa

pink
el color rosa

pig
el cerdo

ballerina
la bailarina

cotton candy
el algodón
de azúcar

flamingo
el flamenco

Which of these pink things has wings?
¿Cuál de estas cosas rosas tiene alas?

worm el gusano

blossom
la flor

shell
la concha

toothbrush
el cepillo de dientes

What color is your toothbrush?
¿De qué color es tu cepillo de dientes?

Purple
Púrpura

purple
el color púrpura

grapes
las uvas

socks
los calcetines

king's robe
la capa del rey

22

What color is the king's robe?
¿De qué color es la capa del rey?

book
el libro

robots
los robots

plums
las ciruelas

candy
el dulce

dress
el vestido

23

How many robots can you see?
¿Cuántos robots ves?

Orange
Naranja

24

orange
el color naranja

pumpkin
la calabaza

starfish
la estrella de mar

carrot
la zanahoria

fish
el pez

What color is the carrot top?
¿De qué color es la parte de arriba de la zanahoria?

orange
la naranja

slippers
las pantuflas

tiger
el tigre

juice
el jugo

Which orange thing can you drink?
¿De estas cosas naranjas cuál se puede beber?

Brown
Marrón

brown
el color marrón

tortoise
la tortuga

bear
el oso

paper bag
la bolsa de papel

guitar
la guitarra

How many ears does the bear have?
¿Cuántas orejas tiene el oso?

chocolate
el chocolate

log
el tronco

hippo in mud
el hipopótamo
en el barro

nut
la nuez

onion
la cebolla

What color is the hippo?
¿De qué color es el hipopótamo?

Gray
Gris

gray
el color gris

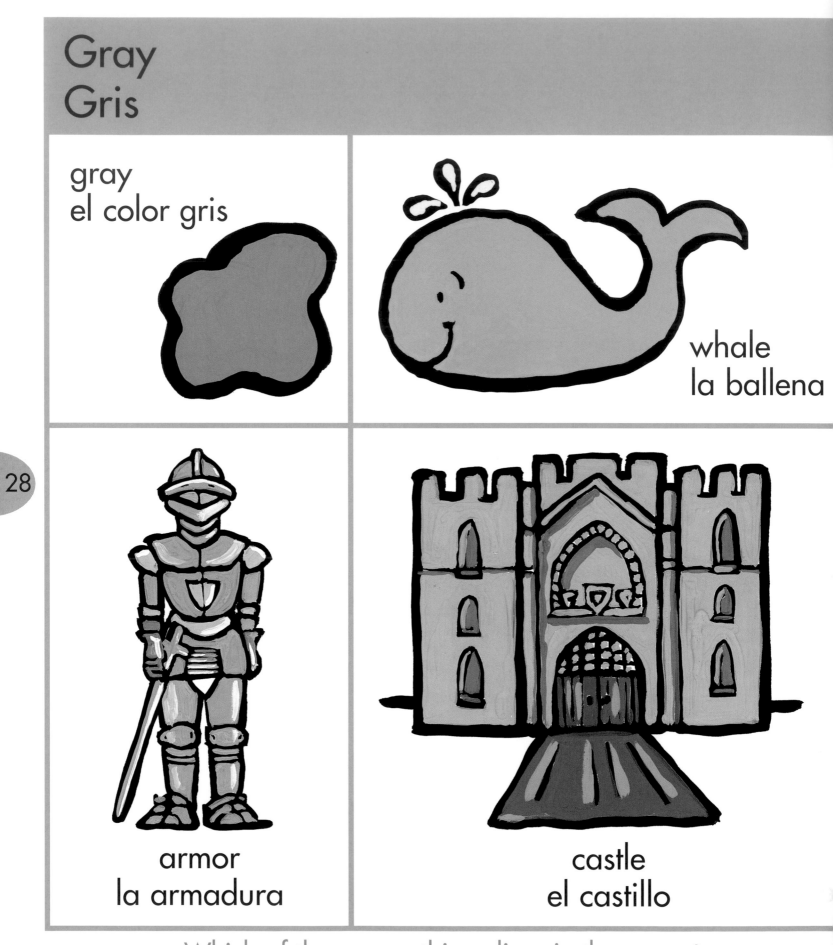

whale
la ballena

armor
la armadura

castle
el castillo

28

Which of these gray things lives in the ocean?
¿De estas cosas grises, cuál vive en el océano?

puddle
el charco

sidewalk
la acera

elephant
el elefante

29

fork
el tenedor

knife
el cuchillo

spoon
la cuchara

What color is the boy's hat?
¿De qué color es el sombrero del niño?

Dark and light colors
Colores claros y oscuros

clothesline
la soga de tender la ropa

closet
el armario

laundry basket
el canasto de la ropa sucia

Can you spot the light-colored objects?
¿Cuáles de estas cosas son de color claro?

drawers
los cajones

coatroom
el perchero de pared

coatrack
el perchero

Can you spot the dark-colored objects?
¿Cuáles de estas cosas son de color oscuro?

Colors at the fairground
Colores en el parque de diversiones

flags
los banderines

slide
el resbaladero

balloons
los globos

teddy bear
el oso
de peluche

32

How many red flags can you see?
¿Cuántos banderines rojos ves?

cotton candy
el algodón de azúcar

Ferris wheel
la rueda de la fortuna

clown
el payaso

ball toss
la puntería con la pelota

What color are the tin cans?
¿De qué color son las latas?

Colors in the country
Colores en el campo

tractor
el tractor

cow
la vaca

pond
el estanque

flowers
las flores

butterfly
la mariposa

34

Which colors can you see on the butterfly?
¿Qué colores tiene la mariposa?

scarecrow
el espantapájaros

boots
las botas

mole
el topo

gate
la puerta del jardín

bridge
el puente

What color is the gate?
¿De qué color es la puerta del jardín?

Colors at the swimming pool
Colores en la piscina

inner tube
el flotador

snorkel
el esnórquel

whistle
el silbato

changing
room
el vestuario

slide
el resbaladero

Is the snorkel light blue or dark blue?
¿El esnórquel es de color azul claro o azul oscuro?

flip-flops
las chanclas

towel
la toalla

swimming cap
la gorra de baño

locker
el armario

ball
la pelota

water wings
los flotadores de brazos

What are the colors on the ball?
¿Qué colores tiene la pelota?

Sorting by color
Ordenemos por color

apple
la manzana

flower
la flor

candy
el dulce

pencil
el lápiz

egg
el huevo

key
la llave

Where should the flower go?
¿Dónde debería ir la flor?

pencil case
el estuche de lápices

vase
el jarrón

candy bag
la bolsa de dulces

key chain
el llavero

39

egg carton
la huevera

fruit bowl
el frutero

What goes into the egg carton?
¿Qué se guarda en la huevera?

Visiting Aunt Julia
De visita en casa de la tía Julia

40

We go to visit Aunt Julia.
Vamos a visitar a
la tía Julia.

Seatown
Villa del Mar

On the way we pass a cat . . .
En el camino, vemos a
un gato . . .

. . . and a grocery store.
. . . y pasamos por la
verdulería.

Then we pass some trees . . .
Vemos unos árboles . . .

Which thing is the wrong color in each picture?
¿Qué cosas están pintadas de un color que no corresponde?

. . . and a playground.
. . . y pasamos por
los juegos . . .

We see a snail in the grass.
En el pasto, vemos un caracol.

A baby waves at us.
Un bebé nos saluda.

Aunt Julia's dog says "hello."
El perro de tía Julia nos dice "hola".

Aunt Julia has made snacks.
La tía nos espera con algo para comer.

What color is your favorite ice cream?
¿De qué color es el helado que más te gusta?

Mixing colors
Mezclemos los colores

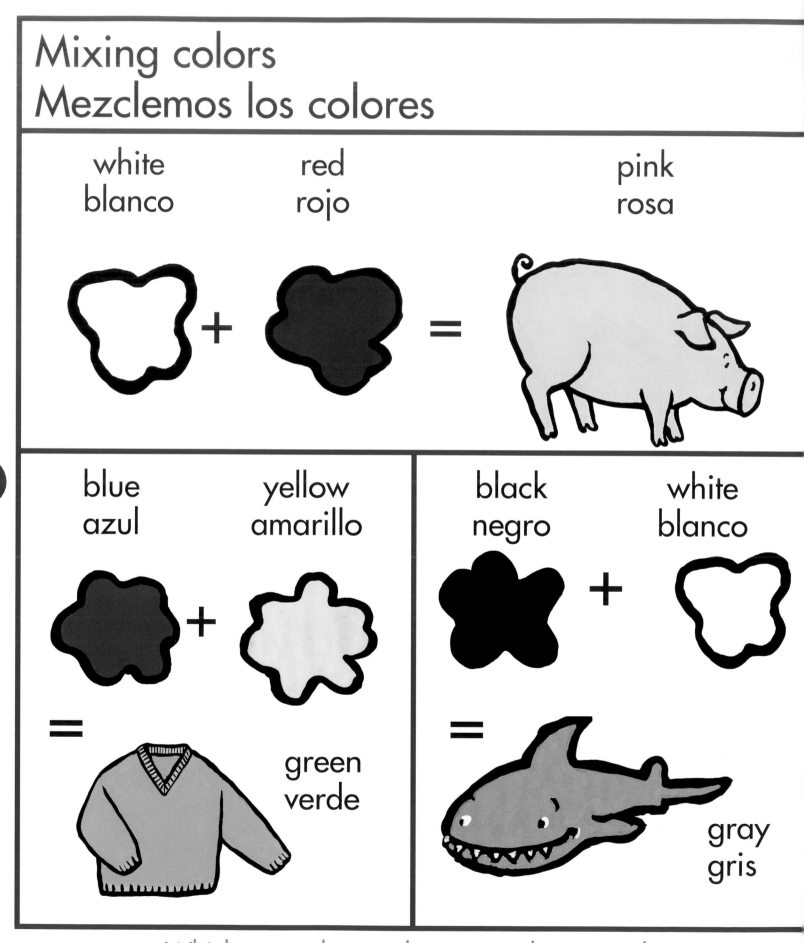

white
blanco

red
rojo

pink
rosa

blue
azul

yellow
amarillo

black
negro

white
blanco

=

green
verde

=

gray
gris

Which two colors make green when mixed?
¿Con la mezcla de qué dos colores se forma el verde?

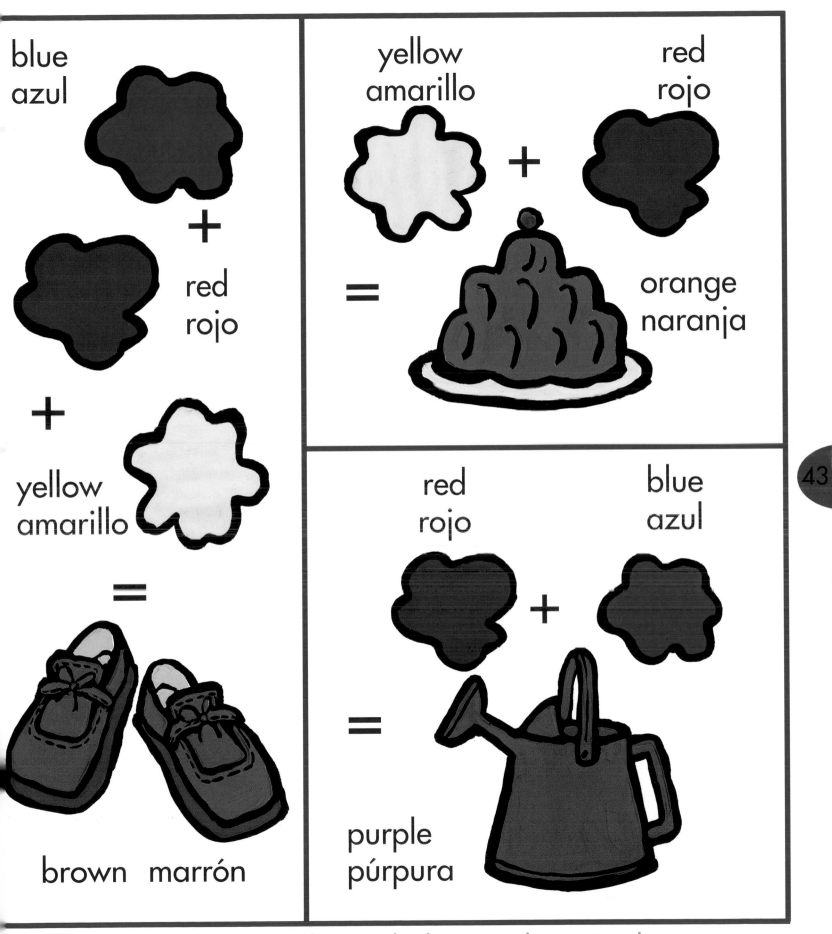

blue
azul

+

red
rojo

+

yellow
amarillo

=

brown marrón

yellow
amarillo

+

red
rojo

=

orange
naranja

red
rojo

+

blue
azul

=

purple
púrpura

Which three colors make brown when mixed?
¿Con la mezcla de qué tres colores se forma el marrón?

Color patterns
Secuencias de colores

scarf
la bufanda

gloves   los guantes

stepping-stones
el camino de piedras

flowers   las flores

44

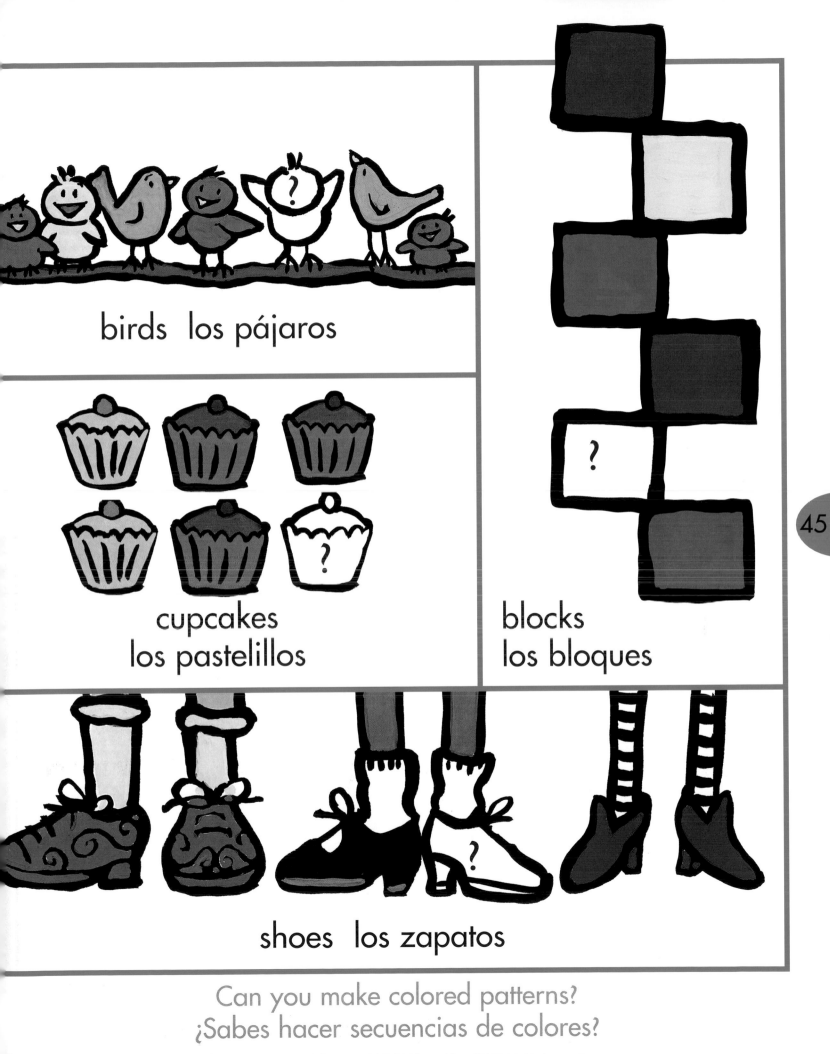

birds los pájaros

cupcakes
los pastelillos

blocks
los bloques

shoes los zapatos

45

Can you make colored patterns?
¿Sabes hacer secuencias de colores?

Who lives where?
¿Dónde vive cada uno?

cat
el gato

bird
el pájaro

rabbit
el conejo

46

dog
el perro

hamster
el hámster

Where does the bird with the brown twig live?
¿Dónde vive el pájaro con la ramita marrón?

cat door
la puertita para el gato

cage
la jaula

nest
el nido

doghouse
la casita del perro

hutch
la conejera

Who lives in the hutch?
¿Quién vive en la conejera?

Now I know . . . / Ahora sé . . .

Goldilocks and the Three Bears

Caralyn Buehner & Mark Buehner

Dial Books for Young Readers

To Matthew

DIAL BOOKS FOR YOUNG READERS
A division of Penguin Young Readers Group
Published by The Penguin Group
Penguin Group (USA) Inc., 375 Hudson Street, New York, NY 10014, U.S.A.
Penguin Group (Canada), 90 Eglinton Avenue East, Suite 700, Toronto, Ontario, Canada M4P 2Y3 (a division of Pearson Penguin Canada Inc.)
Penguin Books Ltd, 80 Strand, London WC2R 0RL, England
Penguin Ireland, 25 St. Stephen's Green, Dublin 2, Ireland (a division of Penguin Books Ltd)
Penguin Group (Australia), 250 Camberwell Road, Camberwell, Victoria 3124, Australia (a division of Pearson Australia Group Pty Ltd)
Penguin Books India Pvt Ltd, 11 Community Centre, Panchsheel Park, New Delhi - 110 017, India
Penguin Group (NZ), Cnr Airborne and Rosedale Roads, Albany, Auckland 1310, New Zealand (a division of Pearson New Zealand Ltd)
Penguin Books (South Africa) (Pty) Ltd, 24 Sturdee Avenue, Rosebank, Johannesburg 2196, South Africa
Penguin Books Ltd, Registered Offices: 80 Strand, London WC2R 0RL, England

Text copyright © 2007 by Caralyn Buehner
Pictures copyright © 2007 by Mark Buehner
The publisher does not have any control over and does not assume any responsibility for author or third-party websites or their content.
Designed by Lily Malcom
Text set in Garamond
Manufactured in China on acid-free paper
10 9 8 7 6 5 4 3 2 1

Library of Congress Cataloging-in-Publication Data
Buehner, Caralyn.
  Goldilocks and the three bears / Caralyn Buehner ; pictures by Mark Buehner.
    p. cm.
Summary: In this variation on the classic folktale, a rhyming, rope-skipping little girl
rudely helps herself to the belongings of a genteel family of bears.
  ISBN-13 978-0-8037-2939-1
[1. Folklore. 2. Bears—Folklore.] I. Goldilocks and the three bears English. II. Buehner, Mark, ill. III. Title.
  PZ8.1.B859Gol 2007
  398.22—dc22   2005036401

The art was prepared by using oil paints over acrylics.

Readers, see if you can find a cat, a rabbit, and a Tyrannosaurus rex hidden in each picture

Once upon a time, in a little house in the woods, there lived a family of bears. They were Papa Bear, Mama Bear, and Little Wee Bear.

Every morning the bear family sat down to eat breakfast, and every morning their breakfast was the same: a bowl of porridge. But one morning, no one was able to eat any porridge at all.

"This porridge is TOO HOT!" Papa Bear exclaimed, after tasting a bite from his great big bowl.

Mama Bear took a small nibble of the small bit of porridge from her medium-sized bowl. "Oh dear," she said. "It *is* too hot."

Little Wee Bear, who loved porridge more than anything, took the biggest bite he could from his little wee bowl. When Mama and Papa looked at him, he tried to say, "My porridge is JUST RIGHT," but because his mouth was so full it sounded like: "My porch has a bus light."

"Hmmmmm," said Papa Bear.

"I know what we'll do," said Mama Bear. "Let's all go for a walk. By
the time we come back home, our porridge will be perfect." So Papa Bear
grabbed his hat, and Mama Bear grabbed Little Wee Bear's hand. Little
Wee Bear tried to grab his bowl of porridge, but Mama Bear was already
out the door.

Off they lumbered down the path.

The bear family was hardly out of sight when a little girl with yellow
curls came skipping rope down the path. She skipped right up to the little
house, pounded on the door, and sang:

"Tra-la-la and tee-hee-hee.
Won't you come and jump with me?"

Of course, no one was home, so no one answered.

The little girl, whose name was Goldilocks, tried again. "Hey!" She banged on the door, and this time it flew open. Goldilocks skipped into the living room without missing a step. When she saw the three bears' chairs, she chanted:

"Big chair, middle chair, little chair too,
Somebody's here to *bounce* on you!"

Goldilocks pulled herself up on Papa Bear's big chair and jumped.

"This chair has no bounce at all . . . "

Next she climbed on Mama Bear's medium-sized chair, but as soon as
she tried to stand up, she sank right down inside.

"This chair makes me feel so small . . . "

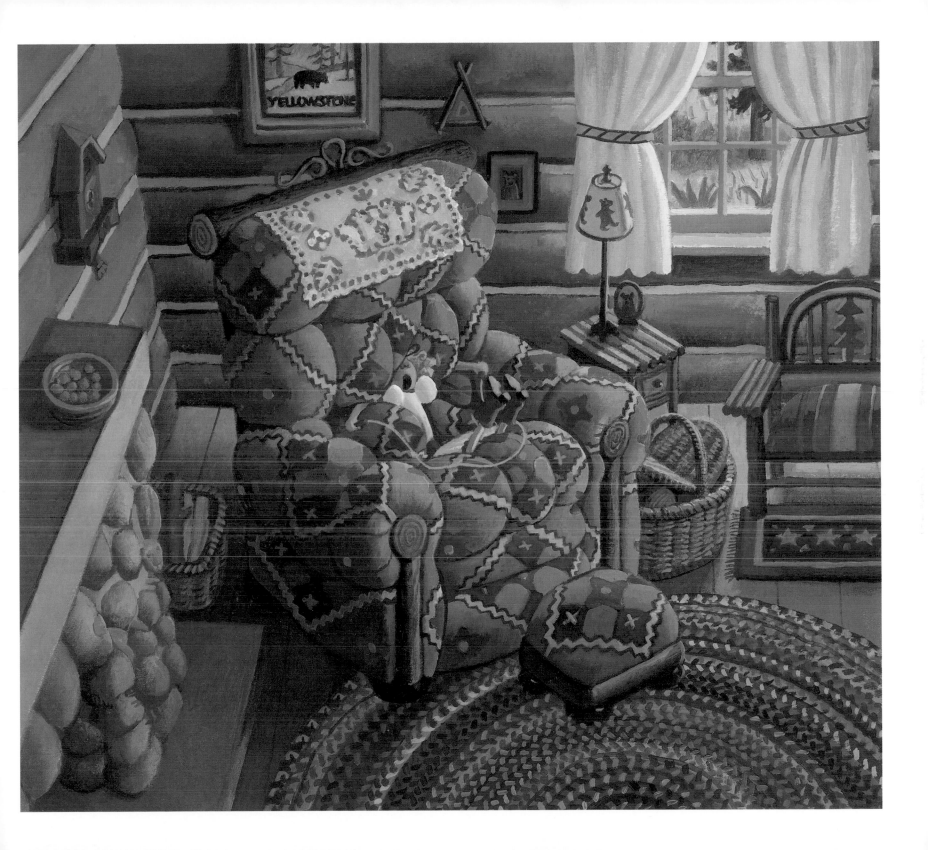

Then Goldilocks looked over at the little wee chair for Little Wee Bear and grinned.

"But *that* chair looks like it's just right.
I'll jump me up an appetite!"

She climbed up on the little wee chair. She jumped, and the chair bounced. Goldilocks jumped and bounced, jumped and bounced until she jumped right through the seat of the little wee chair.

"Oopsy-daisy! What a mess!" She giggled. "Bounced a bit too much, I guess." But she hopped right up when she saw the three bowls of porridge on the table and started skipping rope again.

"Porridge, porridge, sittin' in a bowl,
I'm gonna eat until I'm full!"

Goldilocks tasted a spoonful of porridge from the great big bowl.

"OUCH!" She spit out the huge mouthful of porridge. "This porridge is too hot!"

Next Goldilocks helped herself to a spoonful of porridge from the medium-sized bowl.

She shivered. "This one certainly is not!"

Then Goldilocks tasted a spoonful of the porridge in the little wee bowl.

"Yum-yum!" she mumbled. "Finally! This porridge tastes just right to me!"

Goldilocks ate and ate until there wasn't even one bit left
in the little wee bowl. Then she let out an enormous yawn.

"Goodness, I'm a sleepyhead!
I think I'll jump right into bed!"

Goldilocks skipped up the stairs.

When she saw Papa Bear's great big bed, she climbed
up and flopped back on the pillow.
Immediately she sat up, rubbing her head.
"This bed feels like a big old brick!"

She climbed onto the silky medium-sized bed that was
Mama Bear's. But as soon as she lay down, she slid off the
end of the bed and bounced onto the floor.
"This bed here is much too slick!"
Then Goldilocks spied Little Wee Bear's little wee bed.

"Oh, I hope with all my might that
This wee bed will be *just right . . .*"

Goldilocks tucked herself in the cozy little bed,
with her jump rope curled up beside her. Soon she
was sound asleep.

Meanwhile, Mama Bear, Papa Bear, and Little Wee Bear were just
returning from their walk.

They were very hungry, but when they saw that the door to their house was open, they stopped.

"How very strange!" said Papa Bear.

"Do you think someone's inside?" asked Mama Bear.

"Maybe it's a wild beast!" Little Wee Bear squealed.

The bear family hurried into the living room. There was no mistake about it. "Someone's been sitting in my chair!" exclaimed Papa Bear.

"Someone's been sitting in my chair!" cried Mama Bear.

"Look!" Little Wee Bear's eyes grew very big as he pointed to the mess on the floor. "Something's been sitting in my chair too, and broke it to bits! Maybe it was a monster!"

Then the three bears saw the table.
"SOMEONE'S BEEN EATING MY PORRIDGE!" roared Papa Bear.
"Someone's been eating *my* porridge!" wailed Mama Bear.
Little Wee Bear looked sadly at his bowl. "Something has *eaten* my porridge. I think it was an alien!"

The three bears were very disturbed. Together they tiptoed up to the bedroom.

"My bed!" Papa Bear sputtered. "Someone's been lying on my bed!"

"Look!" Mama Bear whispered. "Someone's been lying on my bed too."

"Something's been lying on my bed"—Little Wee Bear pointed to his little wee bed—"and I think it's still there!"

The three bears crept over to the little wee bed. When they saw Goldilocks, they were very frightened.

"It's a wild beast!" Papa Bear growled.

"It's a monster!" moaned Mama Bear.

"It's an alien!" Little Wee Bear whispered excitedly.

The bear family didn't know what to do. Finally Little Wee Bear reached out and poked the jump rope.

Goldilocks's eyes popped open.

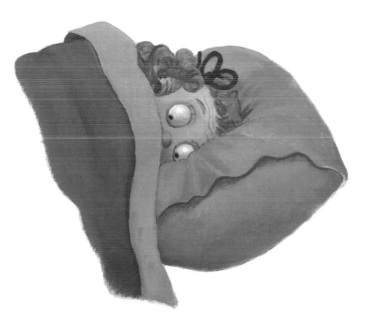

"Eeeeeeek!" cried the three bears.

"Eeeeeeek!" screamed Goldilocks. Then she threw off the covers and sprang out of bed.

"Pardon me if I don't stay . . .
Don't feel like jumping anyway!"

Goldilocks leaped out of the window and ran away before the three
bears had even stopped yelling.

The bears watched until Goldilocks was out of sight.

"I declare!" Mama Bear exclaimed. "I'm so upset, I couldn't eat a bite!"

Papa Bear looked at Little Wee Bear, and Little Wee Bear looked at Papa Bear.

"*We* could," they said.

"HMMPFF!" Mama Bear rolled her eyes. But she mixed up another huge pot of porridge anyway.

And this time it was just right.